QUACK and COUNT

KEITH BAKER

Voyager Books · Harcourt, Inc.   Orlando   Austin   New York   San Diego   Toronto   London

www.HarcourtBooks.com   First Voyager Books edition 2004   *Voyager Books* is a trademark of Harcourt, Inc., registered in the United States of America and/or other jurisdictions.

The Library of Congress has cataloged the hardcover edition as follows:

Baker, Keith, 1953- Quack and count/Keith Baker.   p. cm.   Summary: Seven ducklings take a rhyming look at addition. 1. Addition—Juvenile literature. 2. Seven (The number)—Juvenile literature. 3. Ducks—Juvenile literature. [I. Addition. 2. Seven (The number). 3. Ducks. 4. Counting.] I. Title. QA115.B35 1999 513.2'11—dc21   98-7924 ISBN 0-15-292858-8 ISBN 0-15-205025-6 pb

The illustrations in this book are cut-paper collage.
The display lettering was hand cut by Keith Baker.
The text type was set in Goudy Sans Bold.
Color separations by Bright Arts Ltd., Hong Kong
Printed in China
Production supervision by Sandra Grebenar and Pascha Gerlinger
Designed by Keith Baker and Judythe Sieck
SCP   15 14 13 12
4500394967

7 ducklings in a row
Count those ducklings as they go!

Slipping, sliding, having fun
7 ducklings, 6 plus 1

7 ducklings, 5 plus 2
Playing games of peekaboo

Chasing busy bumblebees
7 ducklings, 4 plus 3

7 ducklings, 3 plus 4
Quack-quack-quacking on the shore

Splashing as they leap and dive
7 ducklings, 2 plus 5

7 ducklings, 1 plus 6
In the water playing tricks

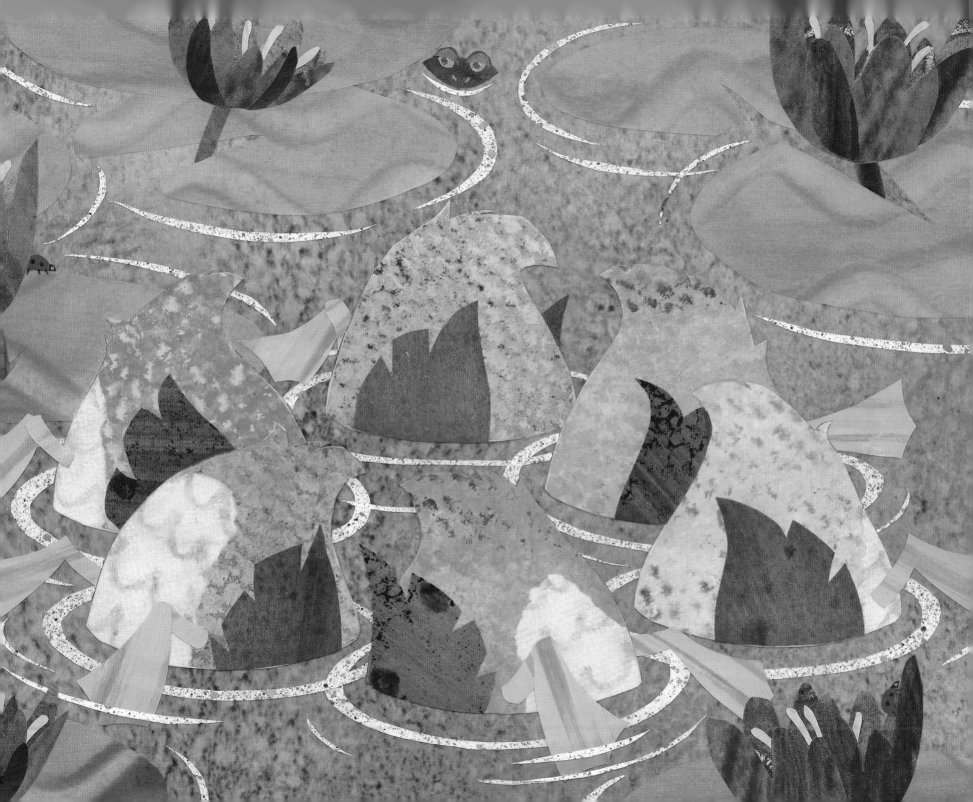

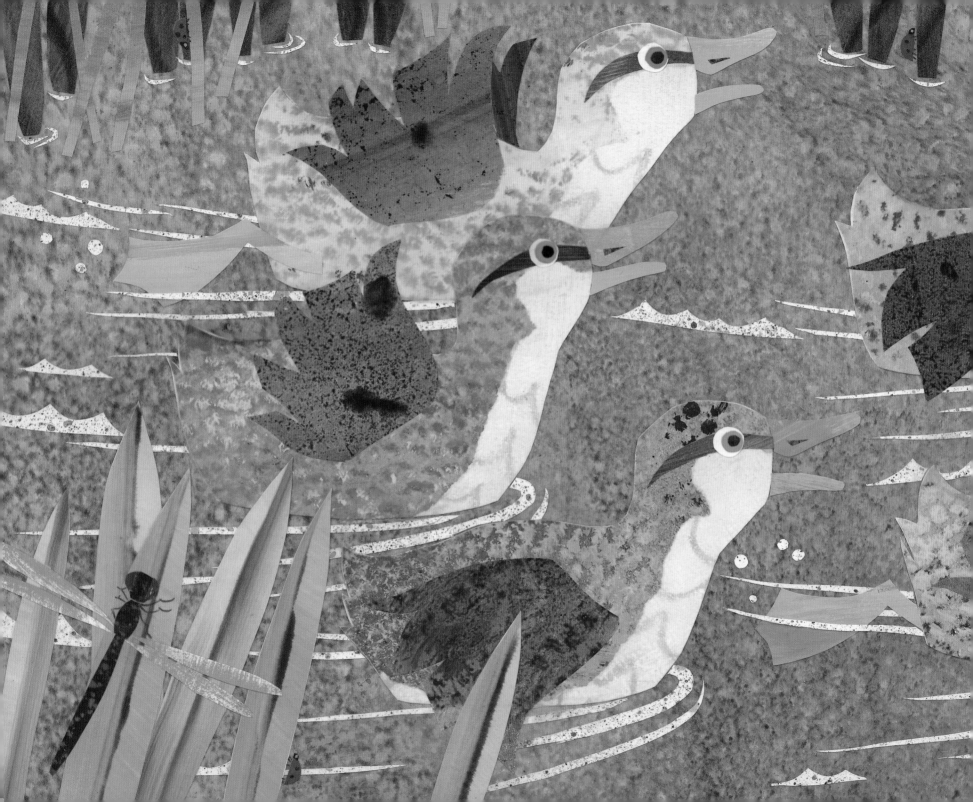

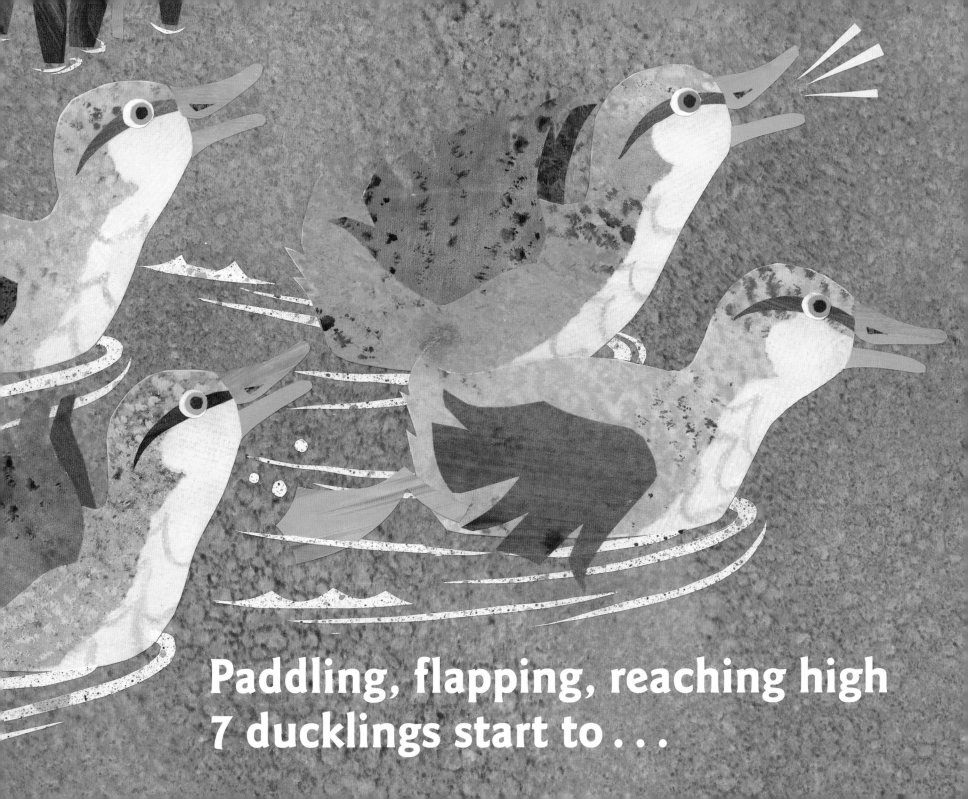

**Paddling, flapping, reaching high
7 ducklings start to . . .**

Up and up into the sky—
Good-bye, ducks . . .

good-bye,

good-bye.